This workbook BELONGS to

the amazing, INCREDIBLE Scrumptious & ENTIRELY gorgeous

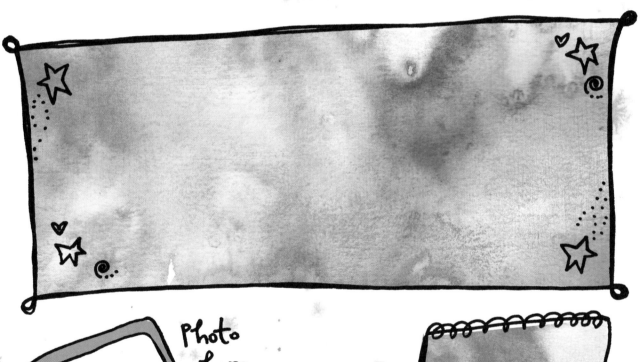

Photo here

Best Contact Details here

We ♥ You:

This book is dedicated to YOU. Because YOU deserve a shining, abundant life that sings to your soul.

We ♥ Our Team:

Big love + gratitude to my wonderful team who midwifed these miracle-babies into the world: Sonya Forrest, Tamara Protassow Adams, Suzi Istvan, Erin Amani, Julie Feilen and Chris Dawson.

We ♥ the World:

This book is printed on recycled paper (Forest Stewardship Council certified mix).

We ♥ Paying It Forward:

A portion of profit from every book sold goes to support a range of world-changing charities including Red Cross, Room To Read, World Wildlife Fund + Kiva.

We ♥ Sharing:

Join our Facebook group of Shining Yearers! www.facebook.com/groups/shiningyear Share pictures of your book on Twitter + Instagram! Use the hashtag #shiningplanners

We ♥ The Internet!

YOUTUBE: goddessleonie
TWITTER: leonie_dawson
INSTAGRAM: leonie_dawson
PERISCOPE: leonie_dawson

FACEBOOK: leoniedawsonpage
WEBSITE: leoniedawson.com
WEBSITE: shiningacademy.com
WEBSITE: shiningyear.com

The Shining Life Workbook:
THE SECRET BEHIND HAPPY WOMEN!

MUST HAVE ITEM

"I've been using the workbooks for a few years now. They've allowed me to achieve some really crazy goals I've set for myself. They are a must-have if you want to create an amazing year."

- Denise Duffield-Thomas, Author of "Lucky Bitch"

A GUIDE TO BUILD MY BUSINESS

"Leonie Dawson's workbooks are SO powerful. I have used them every year for the last 8 years. I gush about them all the time. Whatever I put in these workbooks ends up becoming destiny. I cannot recommend them enough"

- Hibiscus Moon, Author + Crystal Expert

HIGHLY RECOMMENDED

"I love these workbooks and have used them for years for my life and business. Whatever I write in there ends up happening. I highly recommend them."

Nathalie Lussier, Entrepreneur, Ambition Ally

THIS WORKBOOK TURNED MY LIFE AROUND!

"[When I purchased my first workbook] I was struggling with depression and had no faith that I could ever live the life that I saw in my dreams. These workbooks totally changed how I felt...Each year I soak up all the wisdom and fill in faithfully the workbook with all the dreams that I have and all that I want to achieve that year. And I ALWAYS fulfill all of what I hope for and more!"

- Pixie Polly, Artist & Mama

THIS WORKBOOK IS INDISPENSABLE!

"Over the last three years of [filling out these] workbooks I've celebrated so many dreams come true... I use this workbook on a daily and monthly basis to help me plan out my dreams for the year and make them happen."

- Sara Avant Stover, Yogini, Motivational Speaker & Author

THESE WORKBOOKS MAKE DREAMS COME TRUE

"The workbooks have made me a happier, more present mum to my kiddos, and a more patient partner to my husband ...Will I be filling out the workbooks again? You betcha! And will I be recommending them to my friends and fellow businessy people? Sure will."

- Tamara Protassow, Writer & Editor

EASY & POWERFUL WAY TO TRANSFORM!

"The incredibly inspiring and creative workbooks have transformed my life in so many ways...I feel so much more in tune with my needs and I've gained so much clarity... It is so clear to me now that anything is possible. Let the magic begin!"

- Karina Ladet, Intuitive Healer

AMAZED AT THE IMPACT IT HAD!

"Wow! I'm a big forward thinker and straight away this shifted my thinking because first up I had to reflect on the year just past which was incredibly powerful...I ended up purchasing copies for several of my coaching clients so they could enjoy the experience of completing their own workbook too!"

- Belinda Jackson, Marketing, Business and Lifestyle Strategist

I WAS BLOWN AWAY!

"To be honest, I was a bit skeptical when I bought the workbook. They were pretty, but I really didn't think they would do much for me or my business...However, I was BLOWN AWAY by the value offered in the workbooks! I'm now calmer, more focused, and more productive!"

- Shay de Silva, Fitness Coach & Founder of Fast Fitness To Go

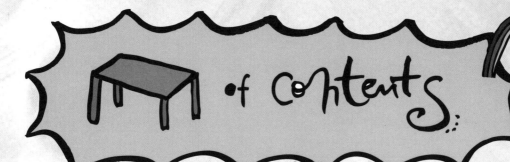

# of Contents

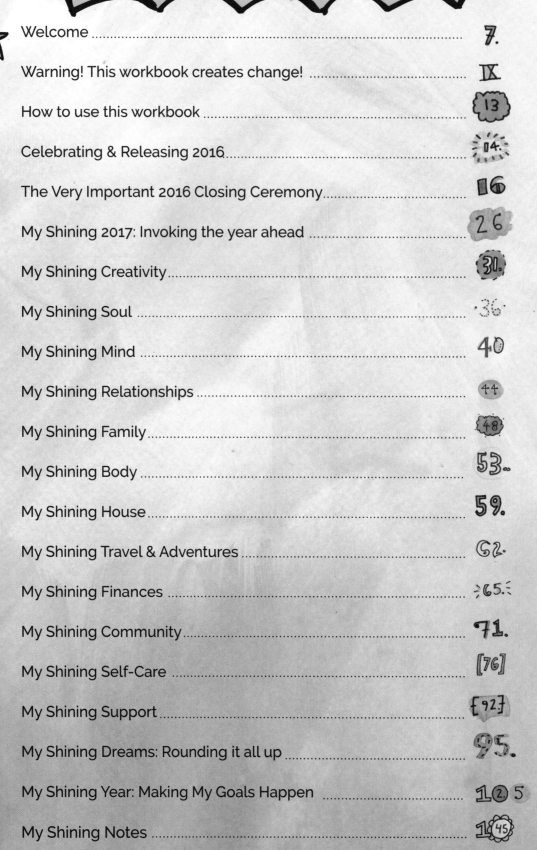

G'day Beautiful Soul

Congratulations on taking this time now to create your year ahead. We all have resolutions, wishes + dreams to create an amazing life for ourselves. Fantastic years don't happen by chance, however. We are the ones who need to make it happen. We need to vision it, dream it, map it out, plan it and **create it.**

This workbook will guide you through doing just that. It is a major miracle maker - not just in my life but for the thousands of women who have been using this book for 8 years now.

Let's go create your

SHINING 2017 NOW!

♡ Leonie

Share your Workbook on Social Media + WIN PRIZES!

JUST HASHTAG WITH:

#shiningplanners

WARNING!
This workbook creates CHange...

In late 2009, I had an idea fall into my (pregnant) lap.

Make a workbook for your New Year's resolutions, the idea whispered.
*Write out your dreams. Find out what happens when you dream your big
dream and commit it to words.*

Ever faithful to ideas that fall into laps, I did. And then it whispered:
Share it with the world. More people need it than just you.

And so I did. I thought it might be helpful to maybe ten others. That would
make me happy – ten lives changed. Ten lives did get changed. I didn't
anticipate, however, that it would go on to become an instant hit. Not only
that, it started making miracles.

Changing lives. Making dreams happen. Since then, over 250,000 women
have created their own shining life using this workbook.

It works. Like crazy.

So dearest, are you ready?

Ready for the ginormous, glorious change that is coming?

Your Shining Year is waiting for YOU!

Results you should SEE from using the workbooks?

More dreams and goals achieved

Increased self-confidence

A tribe of wonderful, inspiring new friends!

Deeper, more fulfilling relationships

Purpose, direction and motivation

Improved productivity!

A wild surge of joyful creativity

Your bucket list being ticked off!

Sky-high levels of joy, love, calm and fulfillment!

→ **INSERT YOUR DREAM HERE** ←
The result I want to see is...

Why is it So IMPORTANT to set & review goals?

When you don't get clarity around where you've been + where you want to go, you can get stuck in the same old place + same old routine.

YOU NEED:

⭐ To spend time dreaming up your vision

⭐ To let go of all the old past stuff + be grateful for it so you can move on

⭐ Support systems to help you make it happen

⭐ Delicious, probing questions to help you get to the soul of what it is you need

⭐ To review your goals regularly so you can take ACTION + bring them into the world!

A goal without a PLAN is just a wish

Want to be in the top (1%) of achievers?

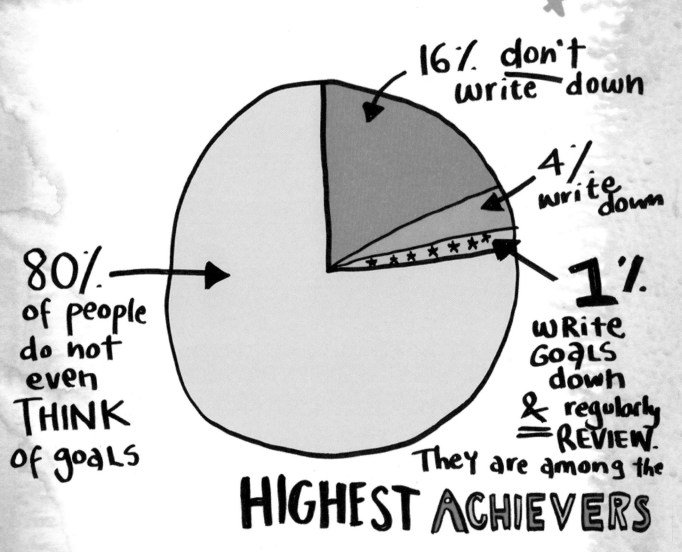

16% don't write down

4% write down

80% of people do not even THINK of goals

1% write goals down & regularly REVIEW. They are among the

HIGHEST ACHIEVERS

Use this workbook as a guide to help you map out your year – so you can make miracles this year!

How to USE this Workbook!

This workbook works, IF you fill it out. Set a deadline for yourself to get it done, and then give yourself the time you need. Make yourself publicly accountable here: www.facebook.com/groups/shiningyear

Don't give up if January's over! It's only too late to plan if you don't ever fill it out!

Make sure you put it in your calendar to review your workbook regularly to keep you on track - I do it monthly for myself, and quarterly with my team. The more you review it, the more your goals will come true!

The 2017 Diary contains monthly check in pages to prompt you to remember and work on your big dreams and goals. (If you need a copy, you can find it here: www.shiningyear.com.) Reviewing your goals at the start of the month keeps them fresh in your mind!

Set deadlines for each of your goals. Set MORE deadlines for each step of your goals. Make sure you put them into your calendar too, then DO THEM.

Put your goals into your Wall Planner. Use your Diary or To Do List pad to break them into small, achievable chunks - use the Magical Mountain Map (page 127) to help you figure it all out!

Aim to make your workbook dog-eared, well-thumbed and deeply familiar. It is your companion and guide for making your life SHINE!

IMPORTANT REMINDER: Do what you can. Invest time in your beautiful dreams. Surround yourself with supportive souls. You can do this!

Celebrating & Releasing 2016

Here's the place where we muck it up

We set our NEW resolutions, our NEW goals, our NEW dreams... without ever taking stock, coming to terms with and clearing all the days and months that have gone before us.

It is so deeply important for us to find the gifts, medicine, lessons, challenges and blessings from the year that has been. Only in doing this celebration and release of the year will we find peace and clarity.

During our closing ceremony over the next few pages, you will begin to see your life with clear, bright eyes. You will find the understanding you've been seeking. From the tangled ball of threads, a rich tapestry will emerge.

And it will be more beautiful, deep & profound than you can possibly imagine right now.

Celebrating & Releasing 2016

You've been sent here on a mission.

To discover every part of yourself. To grow wiser than you ever thought possible. To find the light even in the darkest cave.

2016 happened to you the way it did for a reason. Sometimes there are reasons you cannot possibly begin to know right now. At other times the reason + the blessing are easy to see. Even when it's hard, it doesn't mean it wasn't meant to happen. It's all taking you to where you need to go.

You are getting braver, deeper, wiser, more beautiful by the moment, by the day, by the year.

Let's celebrate + release 2016.

And clear the pathway for the miracles to come.

I choose freeDom. I choose strength.
I choose laughter + courage.

THE
VERY IMPORTANT

2016

Closing Ceremony

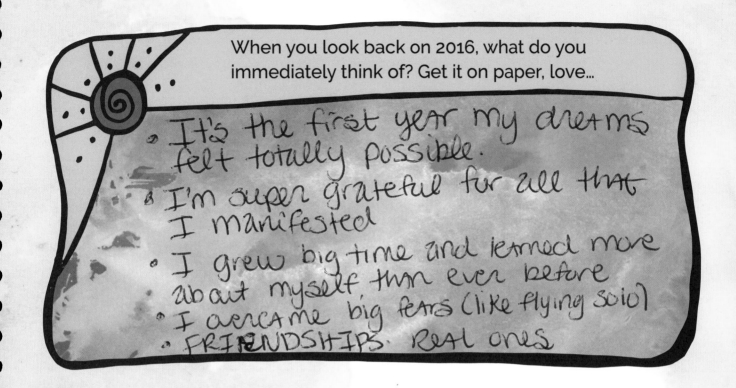

When you look back on 2016, what do you immediately think of? Get it on paper, love...

- It's the first year my dreams felt totally possible.
- I'm super grateful for all that I manifested
- I grew big time and learned more about myself than ever before
- I overcame big fears (like flying solo)
- FRIENDSHIPS. Real ones

What dreams came true during 2016?

- Being invited to be interviewed for a magazine I adore. Inspired catch
- Location independence. Travel + housesitting
- hiring people to help me in business
- finding & deepening soul-Aligned friendships In person.

am a Dream-Maker-Happener

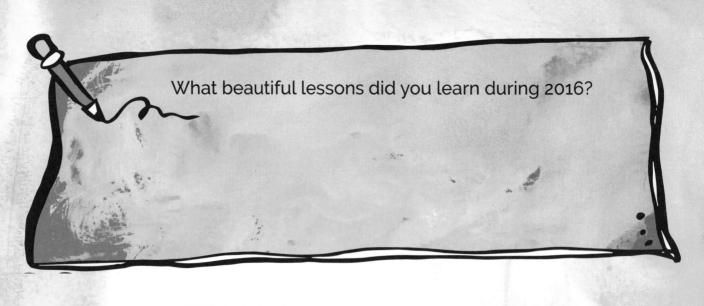

What beautiful lessons did you learn during 2016?

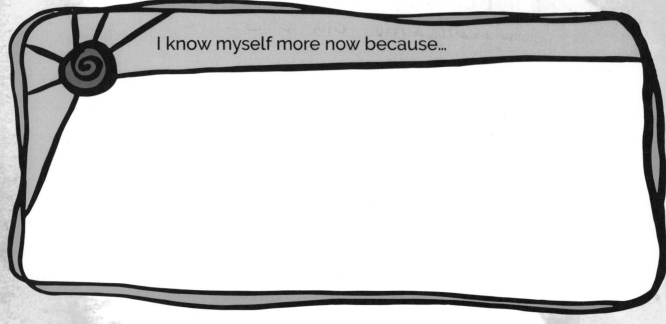

I know myself more now because...

I was transformed this year by...

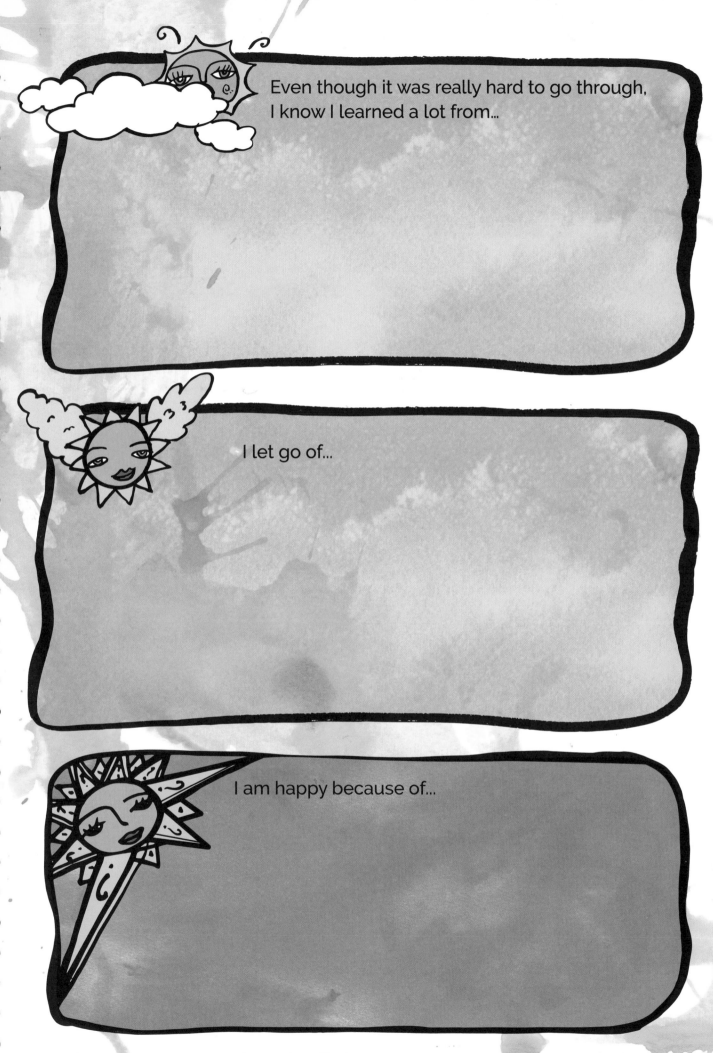

Even though it was really hard to go through, I know I learned a lot from...

I let go of...

I am happy because of...

The incredible thing I discovered about myself was...

2016 led me to...

I am proud of myself for...

What were the areas that felt out of whack, hard to follow or crazy-making in 2016?

What could be done to change them?

What do you need to write, journal or rant about in order for you to feel clear about your life in 2016?

👁 am a DEVOTEE of my dREaMS + a GODDESS of my goals.

A page of gratitude. Draw, write, illustrate, post pictures of EVERYTHING you are grateful for in your life from 2016!

Completion Circle

(place your hand in the circle to receive the energy)

We breathe & give thanks for all that has passed...

We open up to the beautiful possibilities blossoming before us...

We let go & breathe, releasing all that's old & no longer serves us...

We radiate in light & joy... all is beautiful & all is well...

invoking 2017

It's time to dream a new dream.

Time to create an incredible year for yourself, your world, your life, the world.

First comes the THOUGHT.

Then the WORD.

Then the ACTION.

That's how change happens.

are you ready?

YES **NO**

MY Shining 2017

INVOKING THE YEAR AHEAD

Let's DREAM PLAN CREATE YOUR Shining LIFE!

Invoking 2017

Darlingheart, what do you most want to experience 2017 as?

This year, I want to feel...

This year, I would like to release...

This year I want to give myself the gift of...

My very best superpower is being ME!

This year, I promise to myself that I will...

2017 will be the year that...

YOU aRe PuRe ENERGY. Work. Love. Faith.
Commitment. PeRsistehce. PeRSeveRance.

MY Shining Creativity

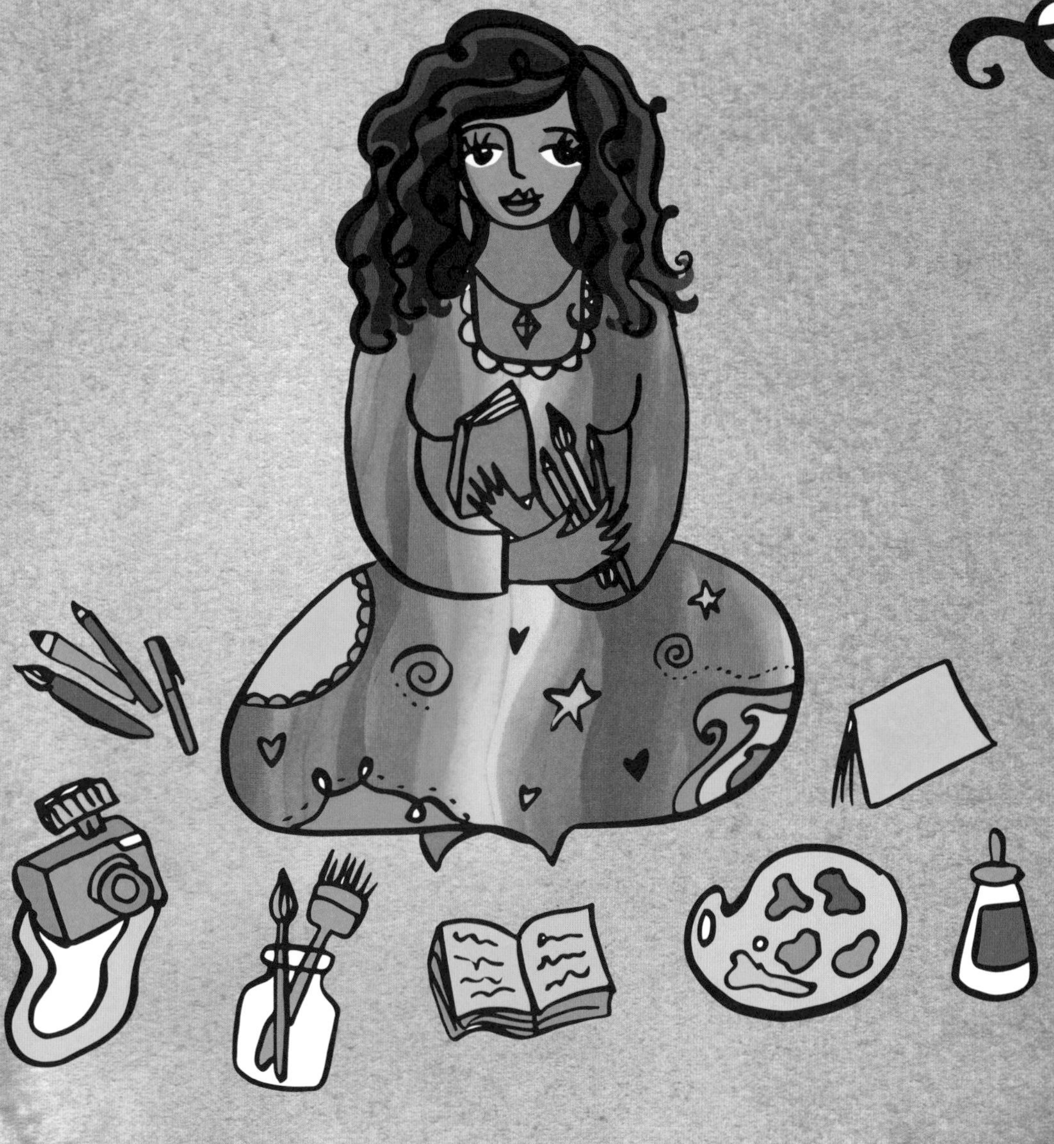

My creative goals
this year are...

What's the major
creative goal out of these
that you want to achieve?

Creative POSSIBILITIES!

CIRCLE THE ONES YOU'D LIKE TO TRY
THIS COMING YEAR!!!
+ HAVE FUN COLOURING IN!!

Photography

WRITE a Song

Learn Guitar

MAKE BIG ART

NEEDLE FELTING

Learn oil Painting

Write a Book

Paper Making

Make CANDLES

POTTERY

WOOD WORK

TRY tie Dying

Jewelry Making

ultimate cupcake baking

SCRAP BOOKING

SCULPTURE

Sing (OR JOIN a CHOIR!)

create mandalas

Make a NATURE MOBILE

Send handwritten letters ♥ ♥ ♥

SEW or DESIGN a DRESS

Make a stained glass Window

Cooking class

Make a MOVIE

Knitting

Add your own

COLOUR in

Day in the Life
SCRAPBOOKING CHALLENGE
ALieDWARDS.COM

365 gratefuls
365GRATEFUL.COM

ARTist trading card challenge
atcpda.blogspot.com

RECOMMENDED RESOURCES Creativity

+ HAVE FUN COLOURING IN!!

The Artist's Way JULIA CAMERON

BIRD by BIRD Anne Lamott

The Creative Habit TWYLA THARP

LETTERS to a YOUNG ARTIST J. Cameron

BIG MAGIC * E.Gilbert

THE RIGHT TO WRITE JULIA Cameron

JUICY PENS THIRSTY PAPER ♥ SARK

LIVING OUT LOUD Keri Smith

THE CREATIVE LICENCE Danny Gregory

Letters to a young poet RAINER MARIA RILKE

Creativity Resources From Leonie

CREATIVE GODDESS E-COURSE

+ MORE

WOOL FAIRY DVD

CREATING WITH KIDS DVD

ART JOURNAL E-COURSE

all available at SHININGACADEMY.COM

My Shining SOUL

My spiritual goals for 2017 are...

We were made to be WILD + GORGEOUS + DIFFERENT. Made to be the soul we are...

HOW DO YOU WANT TO Nourish your Soul THIS YEAR?

CIRCLE OR COLOUR 'EM IN!

FIND YOUR SPIRIT animal

Try shamanic Drumming

Find your SOUL Community or PLACE OF WORSHIP

Journal

MAKE ART

KEEP Candles, poetry, Inspirational Books next to your toilet for Soul Reminders through the Day.

Put your Dreamboard on the Back of your toilet Door!

YOGA

RED TENT

Go on a Retreat

go to a PERSONAL DEVELOPMENT course

Regular Massage/ Bodywork

Sing or Chant

GROUND your feet

ADD YOUR OWN

BRILLIANCE + STAR DUST!

My Shining Mind

What would you like to learn in 2017?

What are your career goals for this year?

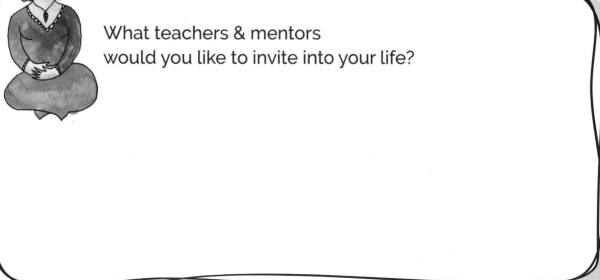

What teachers & mentors
would you like to invite into your life?

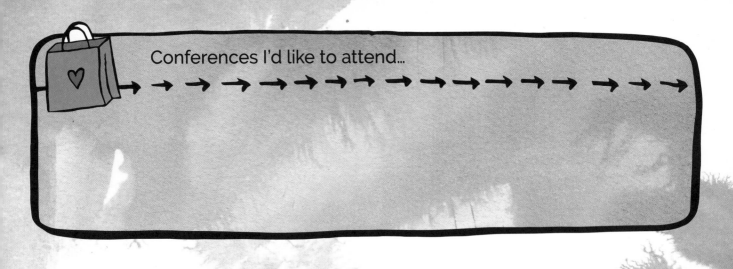

Conferences I'd like to attend...

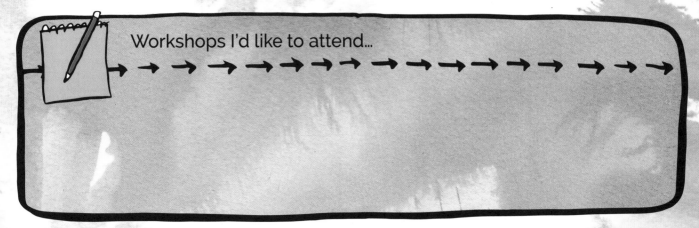

Workshops I'd like to attend...

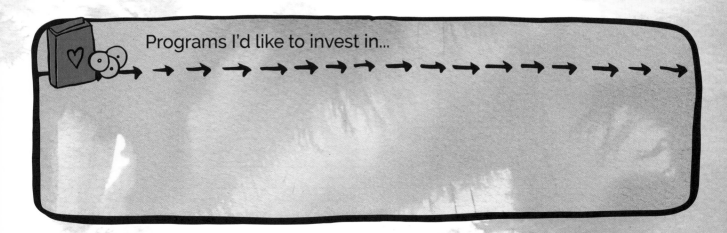

Programs I'd like to invest in...

Books I'd like to read...

CAREER RESOURCES!

+ HAVE FUN COLOURING IN!!

#GIRL BOSS — Sophia Amurosa

Yes Please — AMY POEHLER

I Shouldn't Be Telling You This, But... ♥ KATE WHITE

Martha Rules • MARTHA STEWART

Four Hour Work Week • Tim Ferris

BY invitation ONLY — A. Maybank, A. Wilkis Wilson

Normal Gets You Nowhere • Kelly Cutrone

If You have to cry, go outside — Kelly Cutrone

THE Golden Motorcycle GANG — J. Canfield

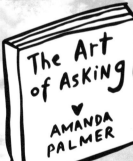
SHARK TALES ~ BARBARA CORCORAN

The Art of Asking ♥ AMANDA PALMER

Double YOUR BIZ Program

BUSINESS Goddess ★ e-course

SHINING 6 FIGURE TEAM

LEONIE'S PROGRAMS IN <u>SHININGACADEMY.COM</u>

> "It takes only ONE PERSON to change your Life — YOU."
> — R. Casey

My relationship goals for this year are...

People I'd love to spend time with or connect with this year...

Don't let the Big Overwhelm of Everything stop you from starting right now!

New friendships I'd like to create would look like this...

Ways I'd like to deepen my current friendships...

Relationship Resources!

+ HAVE FUN COLOURING IN!!

What We Say Matters
.
I + J LASATER

I NEED YOUR LOVE - IS THAT TRUE?
Byron Katie

RELATIONSHIP COUNSELLOR!

If the Buddha Married
♥
CHARLOTTE KASL

FIVE WISHES
Gay Hendricks

TO RAISE HAPPY KIDS PUT YOUR MARRIAGE FIRST
D. Code

So, REAL talk time HERE. The BEST thing you can do FOR YOUR relationship is TO GO TO a good relationship COUNSELLOR. IF YOUR car was broken OR NEEDED A TUNE UP, You WOULD Take it to a MeCHaNiC. THE Same is true FOR YOUR relationship... Take it to a PROFESSIONAL!!!!! ♥♥

THE 5 LOVE LANGUAGES
♥ ♥♥♥♥
G. Chapman

① Love yourself FIRST
② WORK ON YOUR own SHit
③ WORK ON YOUR SHit together.

Leonie's Spirited

Relationships course in
SHININGACADEMY.COM

MY Shining family

My family goals
for 2017 are...

How can you help your children thrive this year?

Some family adventures we'd like to have are...

Some things we'd like to create together are...

Do you have the support you need as a mother? **YES** **NO**

What do you need to do to thrive in 2017 as a mother?

Ways you could make your family life
less crazy-making this year are...

Family RESOURCES!

CIRCLE WHICH ONES YOU'D LIKE TO CHECK OUT THIS YEAR...

MOMMA ZEN
Karen Maezen Miller

THE RAINBOW WAY
Lucy Pearce

You are your Child's First Teacher
R. BALDWIN DANCY

GOOD MOTHER WELCOME
Ingrid Goff Maidoff

+ HAVE FUN COLOURING IN!!

CARRY ON WARRIOR
Glennon Doyle Melton

THE GIFTS OF IMPERFECT PARENTING
Brené Brown

carriecontey.com

stevebiddulph.com

askmoxie.org

Mama Mia
MIA FREEDMAN

handinhandparenting.org

Creating with Kids
DVD

Some of Leonie's programs

Divine Dreaming Meditation

Spirited Parenting Course

HYPNO BABIES MP3s

MOSTLY just TRUST YOUR SELF

CHAKRA healing GODDESS

+ more...

give yourself a BREAK

AND

SHININGACADEMY.COM

My Shining Body

What does your body want more of this year?

What does your body want less of this year?

What kinds of activities will make your body shine this year?

What kind of food will make your body shine this year?

How my body feels right now

Colour in. Collage.
Fill with words...

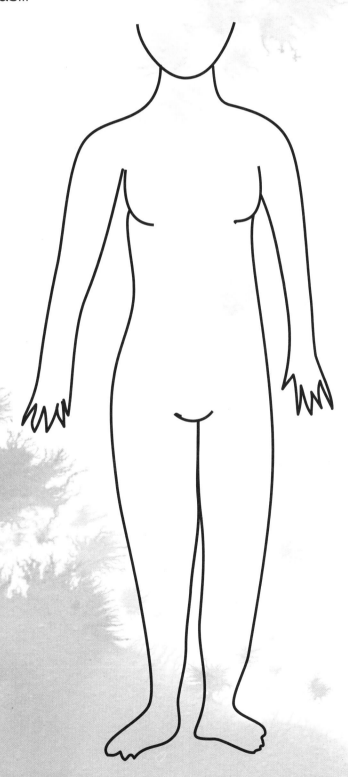

How I'd ♡ my body to feel this year?

Colour in. Collage.
Fill with words...

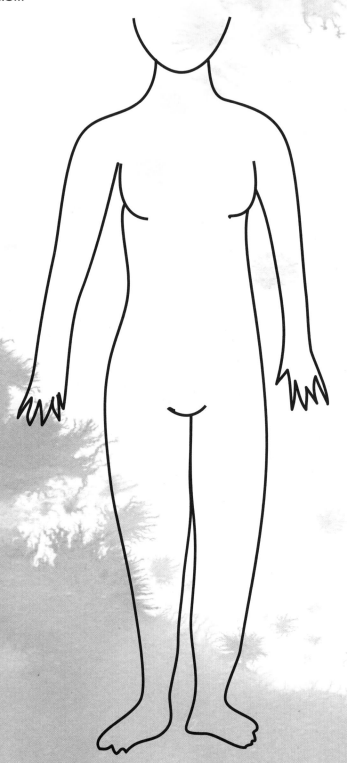

Movement Options

Circle which ones you want to try this year... + have fun colouring in!!

RUNNING

HIKING

ICE skating

SURFING

Swimming

BICYCLING

WII

Kayaking

hula HOOPING

SAILING

Choose your type of Dance

Ballroom

Loungeroom Crazy Dancing

NIA

Ecstatic dance

Salsa

LINE DANCING

ZUMBA

Jive

Five Rhythms

Belly DANCING

WALK ON beach

YOGA

Aqua Aerobics

DISCO Rollerskating

Tai Chi

Golf

MINI GOLF

UNI CYCLING

Circus classes

WEEEE
Trampolining

ROCK CLIMBING

WEIGHT lifting

Volleyball

Ping Pong

ADD YOUR OWN HERE

ADD YOUR OWN HERE

My Shining House

HOW DO 👁🙌 WANT MY HOUSE TO FEEL THIS YEAR?

Do I have a "space of one's own"? A place to create, dream, reflect + be with myself?

YES?

NO?

How could I create that or make my "space of one's own" shine more?

What are some things I could do to make it feel like that?

What are some ways I could invite in more support to make my house shine? (i.e. enlisting family or hiring cleaners?)

circle **WHAT** areas IN YOUR home NEED decluttering;
(COLOUR) the areas in YOUR HOME tHat NEED decorating,

YOUR bed ROOM

kitchen

Bathroom

LAUNDRY

Lounge

DINING

Study

Room

office

ensuite

Attic

Room

Room

Garage

My Shining Travel & Adventures

Places I'd 💗 to visit this year...

People I'd love to visit this year...

What countries are on your bucket list to visit this year?

Movies, concerts or shows you'd
love to see this year...

(If you can't think of specific ones, write & describe an imaginary
one - what it includes & how it makes you feel...)

ADMIT ONE

My Shining Finances

How much would you like to receive this year?

What is your savings goal this year?

What can I do to **INCREASE MY INCOME** this year...

What can I do to **REDUCE EXPENSES** this year...

You Can Do This!

How to be a great money custodian...

Circle how YOU want to develop your fiscal ($) powers this year....

+ HAVE FUN COLOURING IN!!

Pay off all DEBT

Read a MONEY book

learn about STOCKS

Learn about Real Estate

MAKE a BUDGET

TRACK MONEY

Find a GREAT ACCOUNTANT OR BOOK KEEPER

Mint.com

TRY an onLINE money Management system

Find + consolidate super/ retirement accounts

WORK ON YOUR MONEY BLOCKS

ADD YOUR OWN HERE

ADD YOUR OWN HERE

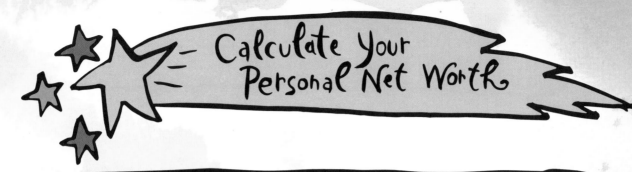

Calculate Your Personal Net Worth

Assets	$ Worth
House	
Car	
Stock	
Superannuation/Retirement savings	

TOTAL ASSETS

Liabilities	$ Cost
Credit Cards	
Loans	

TOTAL LIABILITIES

NET WORTH (ASSETS MINUS LIABILITIES)

ADD YOUR OWN HERE

MONEY resources!

+ HAVE FUN COLOURING IN!!

BAREFOOT INVESTOR — Scott PAPE

Get RICH, Lucky Bitch — DENISE DUFFIELD-THOMAS

SECRETS OF THE Millionaire Mind ★ T. HARV ECKER

ONE MINUTE Millionaire — ALLEN + HANSEN

THE Millionaire NEXT door — T.J. Stanley

Retire Young Retire Rich ★ ROBERT KIYOSAKI

Abundance ☆ P. Diamandis

It's not about the MONEY ♥ BOB PROCTOR

It's RISING TIME! ✳ Kim Kiyosaki

HOW Rich People think — S. SIEBOLD

daveramsey.com

suzeorman.com

THE RICHEST MAN IN BABYLON — G.S. Clason

luckybitch.com

Be a shining custodian of money

MONEY & MANIFESTING WORKSHOP

LEONIE'S SIMPLE Money Planner

7 LIFE CHANGING HABITS FOR AN ABUNDANT YEAR

More Shining Money Resources from Leonie at SHININGACADEMY.COM

MY Shining Community

How do you want your community to change this year?

How do you want your world to change this year?

What causes call most deeply to you?

How much money would you like to donate to charity this year?

$

And to which charity?

How will you donate your time and energy to a charity this year?

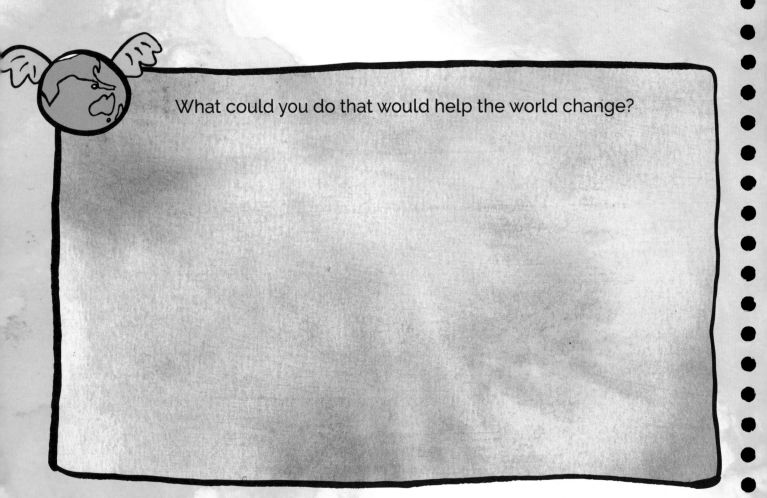

What could you do that would help the world change?

What could you do to make your community shine?

Community Resources

+ HAVE FUN COLOURING IN!!

Creating Room To Read ♥ John Woods

Start something that Matters ♥ BLAKE MYCOSKIE

THE International BANK of BOB • Bob Harris

BEST. BOOK. EVER!!!

CIRCLE HOW YOU WaNt to GIVE BACK to ♥ tHE WORLD tHIS YEAR...

Do a Random act of KINDNESS

SPONSOR a CHILD

Make a loan to Someone in need

KIVA
KIVA.ORG

VOLUNTEER

Plant trees

Pick UP RUBBISH

SPONSOR aN ANIMAL

ask R U OK?

Cook for a FAMILY OR OLDER person who needs it

add your own here

My Shining Self Care

Retreat

Plan a CREATIVE & SOULFUL retreat for yourself this year.

WHEN?

HOW LONG?

WHERE?

WHAT WILL YOU DO?

Now schedule it in! Put it in your calendar! Plan now to make ♥♥♥ it happen! ♥♥♥

Let's get your TIME Sorted!

HOW I CURRENTLY SPEND MY TIME!

Create a pie chart of how your life balance currently looks in the mixup of life, fun, rest & work.

HOW I WANT TO SPEND MY TIME!

Create a pie chart of how you want to create balance in all areas of your life, family, friendship, career & hobbies!

Stop! HAMMER TIME!

So you want to start creating NEW things, yeah?

To do that, you're going to need to clear out the OLD. You need to get rid of old activities, thoughts + habits that aren't helping you move forward. Maybe they once did, but no longer.

WHAT ARE YOU GOING TO STOP DOING THIS YEAR?

Ritual Days

We all know we need to do things that fill us up... it's just hard to remember to fit it in sometimes...

Here's where RITUAL DAYS come in handy!

What are all the things you want to do weekly? Turn them into days!

You could have...

ADVENTURE SATURDAYS

Switch off SUNDays

SpA thursdays

Artist Date mondays...

go-To-Bed – Early WEDNESDAYS

HeaLing FRIDAYS

CREative TuesDay...

My Ritual Days

(Then pop them on your calendar!
I like to use Google calendar & set the day as a recurring event!)

This year 👁 GIVE myself PERMISSION to:

PERMISSION SLIP

PERMISSION SLIP

PERMISSION SLIP

My Mottos

For an easy way to remember what you are trying to cultivate, create some gorgeous mottos.

Here are some examples of mottos for making a magnificent year:

Joy is an option
☆ BE BRAVE
⊙ Reclaim Your Radiance
✦ CULTIVATE MAGIC
♡ Practise Love
✸ embrace Possibility

My Mottos

YOU are AMAZING JUST AS You are...

10 things eye want to celebrate about myself..

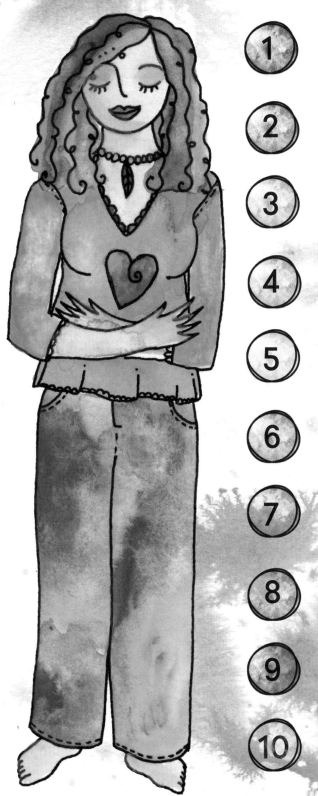

1
2
3
4
5
6
7
8
9
10

 **AN IMMERSED IN LOVE PORTRAIT**

Paste a photo of yourself in the bordered frame... and then all around the photo, write love letters, reminders, messages of support... all the things you need to hear.

During the year you'll be able to look back & feel all the love & soul reminders again.

How would you like to celebrate your birthing day this year?

*☆*Miracles fall from the sky all the time!*☆*

CREATE YOUR OWN
My Shining Habits
LIST

What joyful & nourishing habits would you like to cultivate during 2017? Don't worry about how hard it is to form habits - what we'll be doing instead is creating a poster to remind ourselves each day of the beautiful things we'd like to do.

Some days we might do all of them, most days we'll only get to some... other days we may not get to any of them. All of this is gorgeous & fine.

It's not about perfection or failure. What it's about is reminding ourselves of the sacred toolkit of activities we have available to us.

Brainstorm what amazing habits you'd like to include + create your own poster. I've included a blank one you can fill out & two examples you can draw inspiration from. You can do it!

THINGS TO THINK ABOUT
WHEN CREATING
My Shining Habits

 Make them sound like fun. Use words that lift you + get you excited to do it.

 Make your habits feel achievable. On my list I say to move for five minutes - even though I almost always do way more. If I wrote it down as moving for 15 minutes, it would sound like too much for me & I would avoid it like crazy. Make it achievable so when you do get it done, you'll feel that gorgeous sense of HURRAH + will continue making habits happen in your day. Any extra you do will be a bountiful bonus!

 Phrase them positively as something to move towards instead of being a "Don't."

 Copy habits that sing to you + listen to your spirit to hear what it needs.

There is a WISE WOMAN
inside you that KNOWS the way...

ZEN Habits

1. Set your 3 M.I.T.'s at the start
   Most Important Tasks
   of each work session

2. Whenever you feel DISHEVELLED Declutter

3. "move a muscle to move a mood"
   -Julia Cameron

4. Keep a gratitude journal

5. Eat GREEN THINGS or have a GREEN Smoothie

6. Have a TECH FREE bedroom

7. Take Sabbath

8. Monofocus

Leonie's Shining Habits

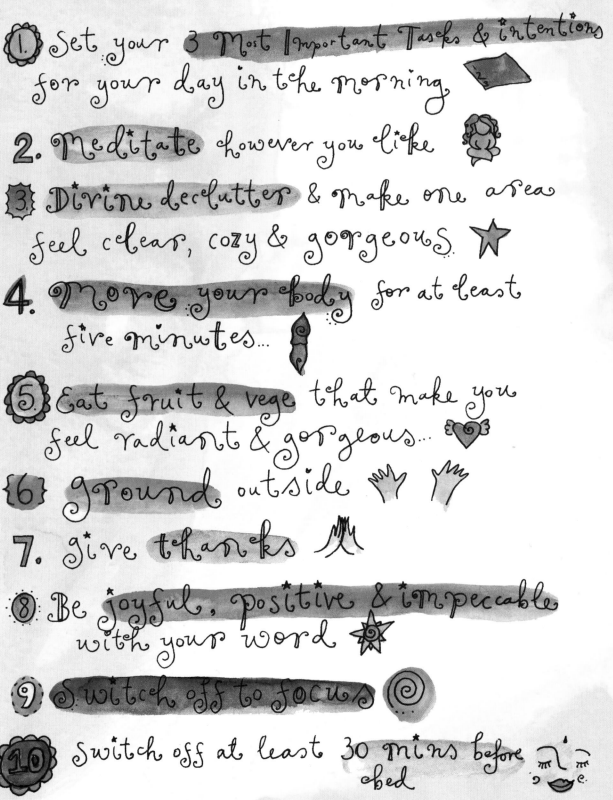

1. Set your **3 Most Important Tasks & intentions** for your day in the morning

2. **Meditate** however you like

3. **Divine declutter** & make one area feel clear, cozy & gorgeous

4. **Move your body** for at least five minutes...

5. **Eat fruit & vege** that make you feel radiant & gorgeous...

6. **ground** outside

7. **give thanks**

8. **Be joyful, positive & impeccable** with your word

9. **Switch off to focus**

10. Switch off at least 30 mins before bed

My Shining Habits

MY Shining Support

Do you have enough support in your life to thrive and shine right now in 2017?
(It's okay. There are no wrong answers. Honesty is gold!)

YES **NO**

If you were fully supported in every area of your life, what would that look like?
(Don't hold back here! It's okay to dream big!)

Make boundaries your besties!

My Medicine BAG

What can you turn to when you are running
low on energy or inspiration?
Friends, books, self-comfort, activities, healing tools.

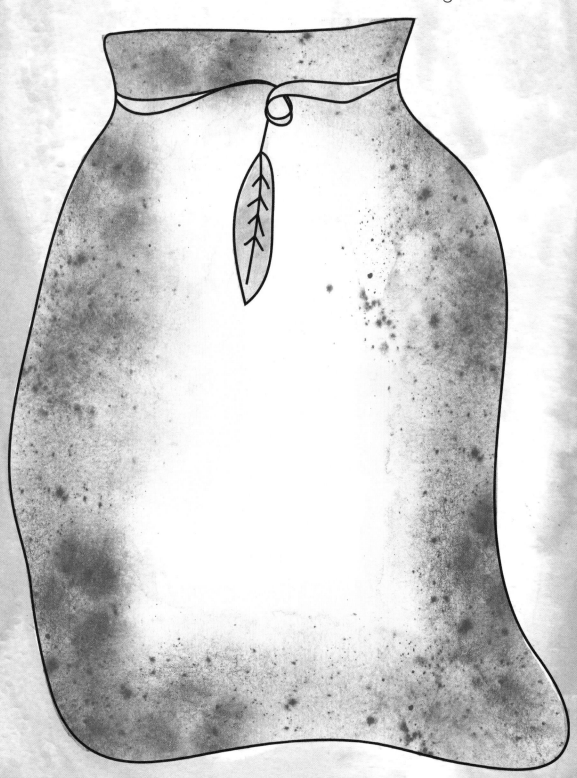

MY Shining Dreams

ROUNDING IT ALL UP

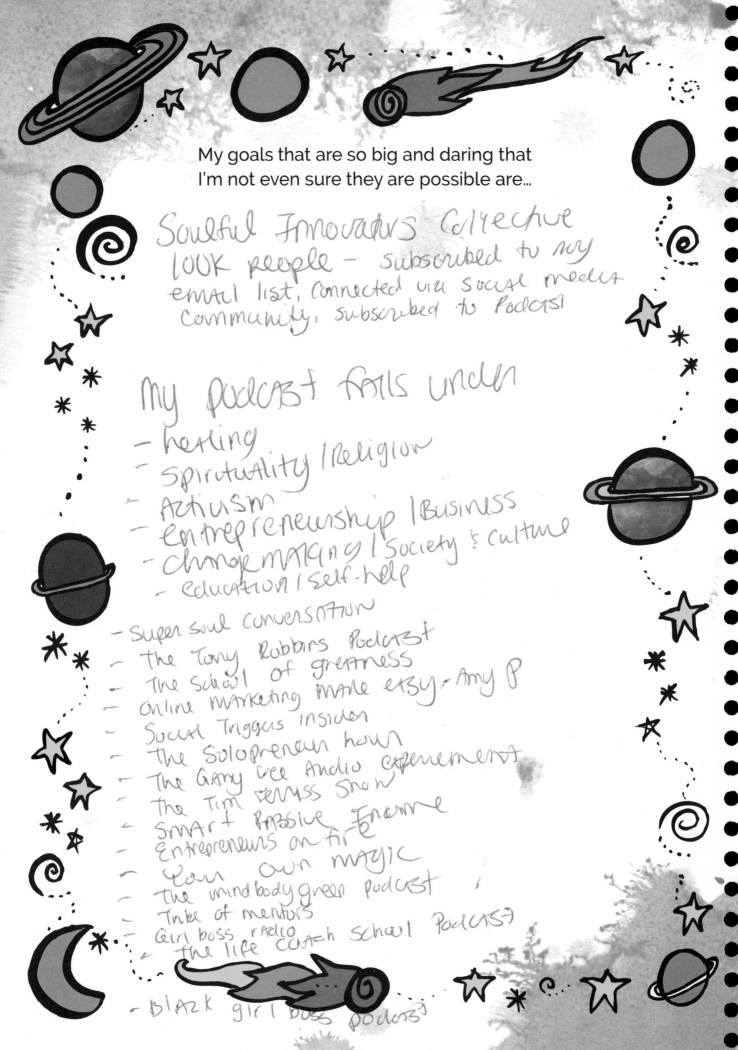

My goals that are so big and daring that
I'm not even sure they are possible are...

Soulful Innovators Collective
100K people - subscribed to my
email list, connected via social media
community, subscribed to Podcast

My Podcast falls under
- healing
- spirituality / religion
- activism
- entrepreneurship / business
- changemaking / society & culture
- education / self-help

- Super soul conversation
- The Tony Robbins Podcast
- The School of greatness
- Online marketing made easy - Amy P
- Social Triggers insider
- The Solopreneur hour
- The Gary Vee Audio experiment
- The Tim Ferriss Show
- Smart Passive Income
- Entrepreneurs on fire
- You own magic
- The mindbodygreen Podcast
- Tribe of mentors
- Girl boss radio
- The life coach school Podcast

- Black girl boss podcast

100 things to do in 2017

These can be silly, fun, joyful, big, creative...
a culmination of all your goals, or totally new ones!

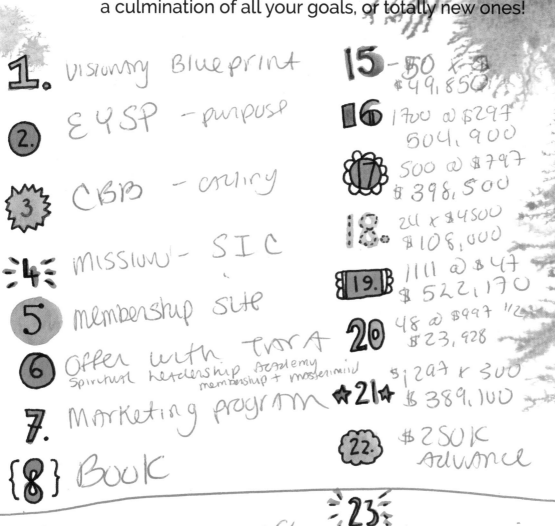

1. Visionary Blueprint
2. EYSP - purpose
3. CBB - calling
4. Mission - SIC
5. membership site
6. Offer with ThorA
   Spiritual Leadership Academy
   membership + mastermind
7. Marketing program
{8} Book

IX. $2,246,448
10.
11. ICONIC SOUL Ideology
12.
13.
04.

15. 50 x $
    $49,850
16. 1700 @ $297
    504,900
17. 500 @ $797
    $398,500
18. 24 x $4500
    $108,000
19. 1111 @ $47
    $522,170
20. 48 @ $997 "12
    $23,928
21. $1297 x 300
    $389,100
22. $250K Advance
23.
{24}
25. Launch A Black Hoodie line
26. Earn $108,000 in Affiliate income
27. - Soulful Innovator
28. - Purpose (calling) mission
29.

30

31.

32

·33·

·34·

35.

·36·

37

38·

39

40

41.

42

[43]

44

45

·46·

47.

48

49.

50

51

·52·

53.

{54.}

55.

56

57

(58)

59.

60

61.

62.

 64.

65.

66.

67.

68

69.

70.

71.

72

{73}

74

75.

[76]

77.

{78}

79.

80

YOU CAN DO THiS.

81.

82.

83.

84.

85.

86.

87.

88.

89.

90.

91.

{92.}

93.

94.

95.

96.

{97}

98.

99.

100.

Word for the Year

If you could pick a theme as a power word, or affirmation of what you'd like to experience & focus on for your year, what would it be?

My sacred word for 2017 is...

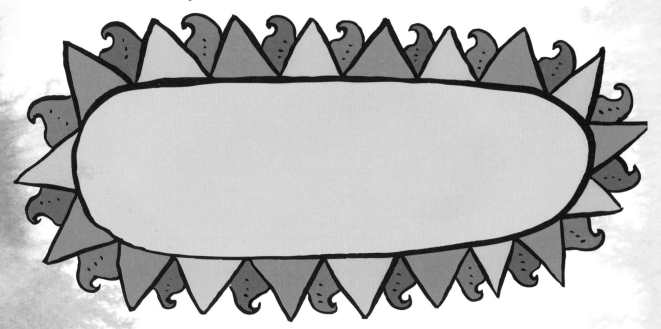

Bonus, optional, extra activity!

Create a collage or artwork with your sacred word on it so you can see & remember & embrace your theme every day. For more on this project go to...

leoniedawson.com/word-year

BRAINSTORM how you CAN Make your WORD of the year Come true for you...

How can you stop or transform the things that don't resonate with your word?

How can you do more of the things that do?

Sometimes it's not enough just to make up your theme for the year. You need to go deeper. Work out what's in alignment with your word and what's not. Then your year will start feeling so much more like the way you want it to!

Consider your word for the year.

What currently DOESN'T feel like that in your life? What activities, times of the day, relationships, habits, emotions don't resonate with it?

What would bring more of that quality into your life?

My Dreamiest Day

I wish this was an assignment we were given in school. I wish we'd been taught how to dream big, and create the life we wanted. At least we're making up for it now, hey lovely?

I want you to write in as much DETAIL as possible your DREAM DAY. Let's talk about your dreamiest day. Where would you be? Who would you be with? What would you do?

I promise you, this is powerful! It's time to become an expert in yourself and your dreams!

notes BRAINSTORMS + Delicious Doodling

Notes BRAINSTORMS + Delicious Doodling

2017 Oracle Reading

I began giving myself "yearly forecast" oracle readings in 2011.

I just scrawled down the themes on a piece of paper.

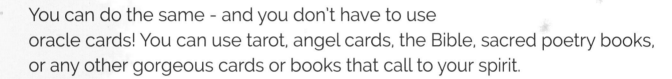

my 2011 card reading... amazingly accurate

It amazed me as I referred back to it each month how accurate & helpful it had been.

And it was so beautiful & useful when it came to preparing for what was to come, too!

You can do the same - and you don't have to use oracle cards! You can use tarot, angel cards, the Bible, sacred poetry books, or any other gorgeous cards or books that call to your spirit.

Just sit with your intention to create a space of guidance and inspiration for yourself, connect to your own shining spirit, and then give yourself your reading for each month of the year ahead.

I used Lucy Cavendish's "Oracle of the Dragonfae" for my reading.

They are my favourite cards to do readings with - they have become like dear friends to me!

www.tinyurl.com/dragonfaecards

There are so many oracle & tarot cards out there that you can use. Choose the one that calls to your heart.

For a list of some of my other favourite oracle cards, head to:

www.tinyurl.com/top5oracle

GIVE YOURSELF AN
Oracle Reading
FOR THE YEAR

Pull 12 oracle or tarot cards for your year ahead. If you prefer, you can also randomly choose passages from the Bible or your preferred holy book, create prayers, randomly choose lyrics or whatever sings to your spirit! There is no wrong way to do this!

Ask your angels, guides, spirit animals or God (whoever you resonate with most) to give you any messages you need to help you shine in 2017.

If you don't have your own cards, try an online oracle... I ♥ Joanna Powell Colbert at www.gaiantarot.com

Write down the card messages for each month... just go with the words that feel the most important.

2017 Oracle Reading

January

February

March

April

2017 Oracle Reading

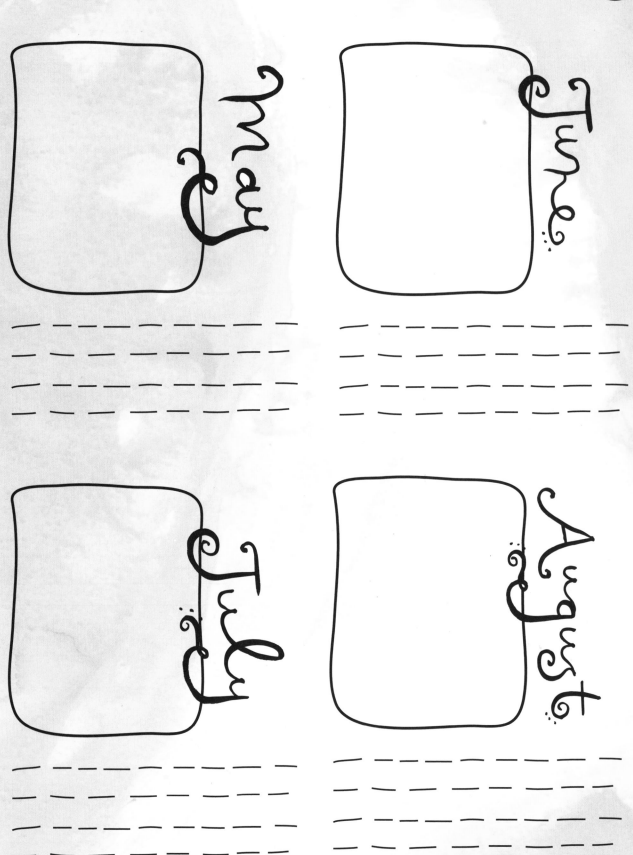

May

June

July

August

2017 Oracle Reading:

September:

October:

November:

December:

CREATE A Dreamboard FOR 2017

Dreamboards are an incredibly powerful tool for drawing your dreams to you through the Law of Attraction. Not only that, they serve as visual guideposts that are not only beautiful and inspiring to look at, but will help you remember every.single.day. your dreams + highest intentions for this year.

And as we all know, what we focus on becomes true. Creating your very own dreamboard right now will help seal the deal between you and your dreams!

Supplies you will need:

 A piece of cardboard, thick paper or canvas in whatever size feels RIGHT To you.

 Glue

 SCISSORS

 MAGAZINES, NEWSPAPERS, PHOTOS + IMAGES

A little blend of OPENNESS, COURAGE, JOY + A SPRINKLE OF HOPE. ☆ ♡ ☺ ☽

CREATE A Dreamboard FOR 2017

Search through MAGAZINES for images + words of THINGS, people, experiences + feelings we'd like to draw into OUR lives for the Next year ♥ ♥ ♥

Cut out images that lift you up, inspire you & make you feel Radiant ★ IGNORE all images + words that feel like a SHOULD.

glue them onto your CARDBOARD until it feels ≥ just RIGHT ≤ to your spirit ♥

PLACE it SOMEWHERE YOU SEE it DAILY. ON YOUR desk, BY YOUR BED, even on the back of your toilet door!

♥ YOU CAN ALSO USE THE FOLLOWING PAGE TO CREATE A MINI PORTABLE DREAMBOARD TO KEEP WITH YOUR WORKBOOK!

Ⓟ You can also use Pinterest as an ONLINE DREAMBOARD. You might also like to create a companion Pinterest board for dreams fulfilled too!

& watch it magically appear!

DreamBoard EXAMPLES

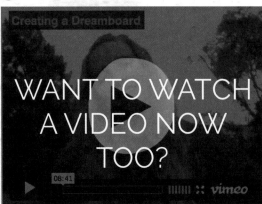

Creating a Dreamboard

WANT TO WATCH
A VIDEO NOW
TOO?

08:41 vimeo

www.leoniedawson.com/dreamboard

Mini Portable Life Dreamboard

THE LIST OF Things To Do WHEN EVERYthing SuCKS!

Our feelings can change in an instant. Fickle things they are - generated by the moment, the situation, our hormones & our perspective. If we can change just one of these things, a great healing can occur.

We can go from rock bottom to, "You know what? I'm okay..." in about 15 minutes. There's a world of difference between those 2 places. All we need to do is remember the things that work for us... the little changes that can make a big difference.

Let's prepare ourselves now... let's write our reminder list of Things To Do When Everything Sucks.

Cut this out & put it in a place you can grab in case of sucktastic emergency... purse, desk, or type it into your phone

My list to de-stuckify

★ go outside for 5 minutes
★ smell lavender
★ get sunshine on my face
★ eat something green
★ have a shower
★ do a 5-minute meditation or breather

SURe! Cut Me out ♥ love!

In case the suckies strike

(1)
(2)
(3)
(4)
(5)
(6)
(7)
(8)
(9)
(10)

Affirmations

Create your own. Collage. Cut out.
Put around your home, in your diary, pockets & purse.

you are ♡ aDoReD

You were born To BE EXACTLY WHO YOU ARE ♥♥

SURe! Cut Me out ♥love!

notes BRAINSTORMS & Delicious Doodling

Create an EVERYDAY MIRACLES JAR

WHAT to DO:

GET a large JAR/TUB/BOX.
DECORATE it Beautifully,
COVER it with the Label
here →

Add glitter/collage/
MODGE PODGE.

THIS IS YOUR

everyday Miracles Jar

WRITE DOWN

your everyday miracles
as they happen oh
Small pieces of paper.

Ceremoniously

PLACE THEM IN YOUR
EVERYDAY MIRACLES JAR
WHILE HUMMING
"EYE OF THE TIGER"

(that, or just fold + pop it in!)

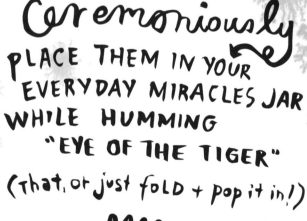

What Kinds Of Everyday Miracles Should I Write?

 Unexpected letters & parcels

 random acts of KINDNESS

 THE DELICIOUS MEAL OR PERFECT CUP OF TEA

 SWEET MOMENTS & DEAR CONNECTIONS

The moment you laugh so hard you nearly wet your pants!

WHEN TO DO THEM

- Find the rhythm that suits you
- Maybe daily / weekly / monthly
- Do with your kids or partner

At the end of the year...

you will have a precious collection of memories to reflect on, celebrate & start your new year feeling gratitude!

cut this out & use as a label for a jar!

SNIP ME OUT! take me with you.

A jar for collecting everyday miracles

How my company turns our GOALS into ACTION

Set a **DEADLINE** to finish workbook

Get copies made for everyone on team ♥ ♥ ♥ ♥

Set QUARTERLY GOALS. Lay out BIG PROJECTS on wall planner.

PROJECT PLAN it!

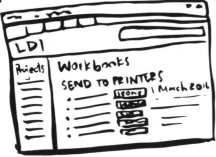

LDI
Projects | Workbooks
SEND TO PRINTERS | 1 March 2016

• Pile all the goals + activities into our project management software

 DRILL down to details— every single task that needs to be done to complete goal

 Assign everything to WHO will do it!

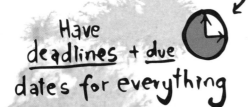 Have <u>deadlines</u> + <u>due</u> dates for everything

REVIEW + CHECK ON PROGRESS **Monthly**

Make your GOALS happen!

Setting your goals is just one part of the process of making things happen.

It helps to think of a *goal* as the top of a *magical mountain* you need to climb.

Getting to the top (the goal!) is not possible with just one step!

You're going to need to climb that mountain one step at a time.

And sometimes, there will be some steps that need other things done to complete them too – which can feel overwhelming, and like the top will never be reached.

Once you have your goal, brainstorm all of the things that you need to do to get there.

List all the tiny steps that have to happen before you get to the top.

STOP! Don't overthink this! Just get them down.

SUPER tip

If your step has more than 1 piece, separate them into 2 steps.

The really wonderful thing is this: the more you hone your steps into smaller pieces, the more focussed you become, because the thinking is already done. You just get to ACTION!

On the next 3 pages there are 3 Magical Mountains for you to fill in. Remember to break your big items into small doable steps, and make a date to DO THEM.

You can do it!

REMEMBER: climbing your Magical Mountain to reach your goal means doing **3** things:

① Write down every task **RIGHT NOW**.

② Highlight the most important ones you need to do first.

③ Schedule your steps into your calendar – **AND DO THEM!**

Magical Mountain Map

ADD Project Name

Write down all the steps you need to take to get up the mountain...

& THEN NUMBER THEM! IN ORDER OF PRIORITY

What support/resources do you need

FOR THIS MAGICAL MOUNTAIN TREK?

Journal what you need here:

TIME

Money

Health

Support

magical mountain map

ADD Project Name

Write down all the steps you need to take to get up the mountain...

& THEN NUMBER THEM! IN ORDER OF PRIORITY

What support/resources do you need

FOR THIS MAGICAL MOUNTAIN TREK?
Journal what you need here:

TIME

Money

Health

Support

magical mountain map

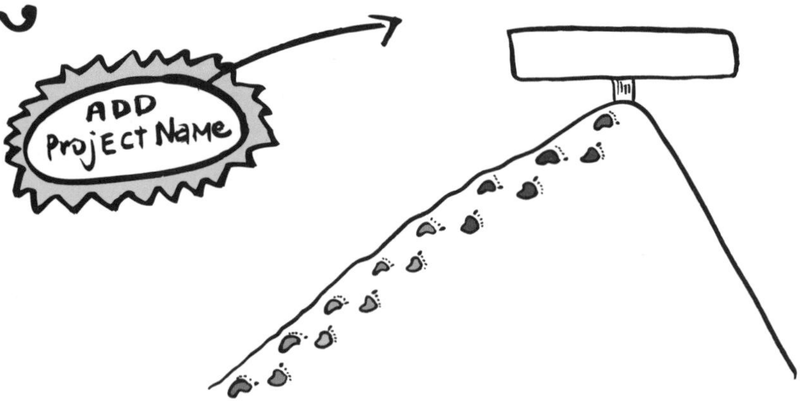

ADD Project Name

Write down all the steps you need to take to get up the mountain...
& THEN NUMBER THEM! IN ORDER OF PRIORITY

What support/resources do you need

FOR THIS MAGICAL MOUNTAIN TREK?
Journal what you need here:

TIME

MONEY

HEALTH

Support

What To Do when you FALL the WORKBOOK OFF WAGON!

1. FORGIVE YOURSELF

2. REVIEW THIS BOOK
WHAT GOALS CAN YOU ACHIEVE THIS MONTH?

4. GO GET YOUR GOAL GIRL!

3. GO PUBLIC.
TELL FRIENDS OR YOUR MASTERMIND YOUR GOAL. ASK THEM TO HOLD YOU ACCOUNTABLE.

Want to SPREAD THE WORD about this book + Receive thank you monies?

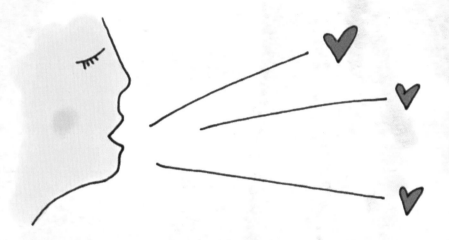

Sign up to become an affiliate (for FREE!) and receive cashola every time someone buys a workbook because of you!

You'll help the people who need this workbook to change their lives AND receive some gorgeous thank you monies at the same time!

SIGN UP NOW SO WE CAN SEND YOU MOOLAH!

www.LeonieDawson.com/affiliate

What is a Leonie?

Leonie Dawson is a celebrated soul-centred life + business teacher, best-selling author and passionate philanthropist leading a multi-million dollar company. Over the past 11 years she has taught hundreds of thousands of women how to have more spirited lives and abundant businesses through her Create Your Shining Year workbooks + Shining Biz & Life training academy.

Leonie has been recognised for her business acumen by being voted a top 6 finalist in the My Business Awards for Australian Businesswoman of the Year, and a finalist in the Ausmumpreneur of the Year Award.

Leonie lives in the alpine mountains of Canberra, Australia with her hunky husband and their two mermaid daughters.

YOUTUBE: goddessleonie

TWITTER: leonie_dawson

INSTAGRAM: leonie_dawson

PERISCOPE: leonie_dawson

FACEBOOK: leoniedawsonpage

WEBSITE: leoniedawson.com

WEBSITE: shiningacademy.com

WEBSITE: shiningyear.com

WHAT IF YOU MAKE

2017

YOUR MOST

Amazing

YEAR YET?

The Academy is one part
BiZ + Marketing
TRAINING FiELD + one part
Inspirational Mastermind
+ one part
Soul-centered Wisdom
to make every part of your
LIFE SHINE

""I've got so much out of being an Academy member that I can't rave enough about it, there are truly no words."

- Emmanuelle Lambert, Yoga Teacher + Life/Biz Coach

"Leonie Dawson's entire Academy of products is incredibly generous. Best purchase of the year!"

- Liberty Montano, Fiber Artisan & Mother

"I've found my soul's home in the Academy: It's gotten me out of a rut, and into my dream business. I am so supported, creative, and confident because of it!"

Charlotte Grace Hunt, Founder of The Happy Hunt

What you GET *in the Academy

The Academy is more than just one single program – it gives you access to a huge range of my products and programs to help you transform + shine in every single area of your life and business.

SHINING BUSINESS
Powerful business training to help you start + grow your dream business abundantly!

SHINING FINANCES
Powerful money programs + spreadsheets to get abundance flowing + your financial life in order.

SHINING MARKETING
Learn how to harness the power of marketing on AND offline to transform your business into an abundance machine!

SHINING HOME
Programs to get your house decluttered + to remove negative energy from your home.

SHINING CREATIVITY
Workshops to clear your creative blocks + become a wildly prolific creative goddess!

SHINING RELATIONSHIPS
Become a better mama + have happier, deeper, more satisfying relationships.

SHINING HEALTH
Cleanses to bring your body into health & radiance.

MEDITATIONS
Healing, zen-inducing audio meditations to soothe your soul.

shiningAcademy.com

Amazing Business Programs

Start, grow & elevate your business with this complete toolkit of business & marketing resources...

"Leonie's business program in the Academy is a veritable encyclopedia of creative business guidance. I'm still kind of floored by all the things Leonie covers in it. Here was this happy hippy beach chick, thriving in her creative business, and willing to share all the millions of things she's learned to get there. Her advice is smart. And generous."
- Christine Boles, Artist

"In the time since I joined the Academy, I've quit my day job, taken my business fulltime , raised my rates twice and worked with some truly awesome clients from around the world!"
- Tanja Gardner, Copywriter

Shining Academy.com

Amazing Life Programs

Get every area of your life shining (from health and happiness to family and home) with these shining, powerful resources...

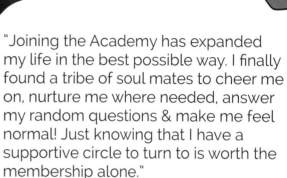

"Joining the Academy has expanded my life in the best possible way. I finally found a tribe of soul mates to cheer me on, nurture me where needed, answer my random questions & make me feel normal! Just knowing that I have a supportive circle to turn to is worth the membership alone."
- Jaci Elliot Dorset, Founder of Happiness Backpack

"The resources and women made available through the Academy were game-changing. The best results were that I stopped doubting myself. Instead of wondering if I was making the right choice, I realized that not only am I making the right choice but I will succeed. I am succeeding."
- Shai Smith, Eco-Friendly Lifestyle Blogger

Amazing Creativity

Get creatively unblocked & overflowing with inspiration with these magical, popular (and proven!) shining creative programs...

shiningAcademy.com

Want It All?

Join the SHINING BIZ + LIFE ACADEMY + get:

- $12K+ value of my programs (including next year's workbook!)

- Access to a community with over 3000+ members

- 70+ courses

All for a wildly affordable $497!

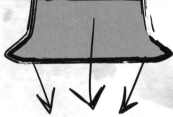

shining Academy.com

My Shining Notes

Notes, BRAINSTORMS & Delicious Doodling

notes BRAINSTORMS + Delicious Doodling

notes {BRAINSTORMS} & Delicious Doodling

Notes BRAINSTORMS + Delicious Doodling

Notes, BRAINSTORMS & Delicious Doodling

notes BRAINSTORMS + Delicious Doodling

notes {BRAINSTORMS} & Delicious Doodling

Notes, BRAINSTORMS & Delicious Doodling

Notes BRAINSTORMS & Delicious Doodling

Notes BRainstorms + Delicious Doodling

notes BRAINSTORMS + Delicious Doodling

Notes BRAINSTORMS + Delicious Doodling

notes BRAINSTORMS + Delicious Doodling

notes BRAINSTORMS & Delicious Doodling

notes BRAINSTORMS & Delicious Doodling

notes BRAINSTORMS & Delicious Doodling

notes BRAINSTORMS & Delicious Doodling

Notes BRAINSTORMS & Delicious Doodling

Notes BRAINSTORMS + Delicious Doodling

Notes, BRAINSTORMS & Delicious Doodling

Notes BRAINSTORMS + Delicious Doodling

notes BRAINSTORMS + Delicious Doodling

notes BRAINSTORMS + Delicious Doodling

Notes, BRAinstORMS + Delicious Doodling

Notes, BRAinstoRMs + Delicious Doodling

Notes BRAINSTORMS + Delicious Doodling

Notes, BRAINSTORMS + Delicious Doodling

Snotes BRAInstORMS + Delicious Doodling

Notes BRAINSTORMS + Delicious Doodling

Notes, BRAINSTORMS + Delicious Doodling